HÄ
THE H

Hagar In a Stew

DiK BROWNE

ATTICA
PUBLICATIONS

Aylesbury 11-08-90

Introducing ...

HÄGAR THE HORRIBLE a hard-working Barbarian businessman. He's in sacking and looting.

His wife, HELGA. She finds civilising Hagar a 24-hour-a-day job!

This is HAMLET, their son, a real problem child! He insists on wearing his hair short, bathing, reading and otherwise behaving in a very unbarbarian manner.

HONI, their daughter, is sixteen years old, and still not married!

But that's not the end of Hagar's troubles... there's also LUCKY EDDIE who must be the most hopeless assistant in history!

© 1988 King Features Syndicate, Inc.
First Published by Attica Publications 1988.

ATTICA Publications is an imprint of Attica Limited
DLM House, Edinburgh Way, Harlow, Essex, CM20 2HL, England.

ISBN 1 85176 175 6

Printed and bound in Great Britain by Cox & Wyman Ltd., Reading.

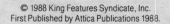

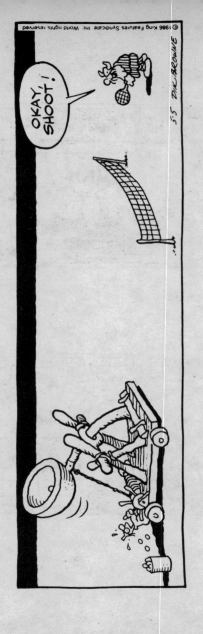

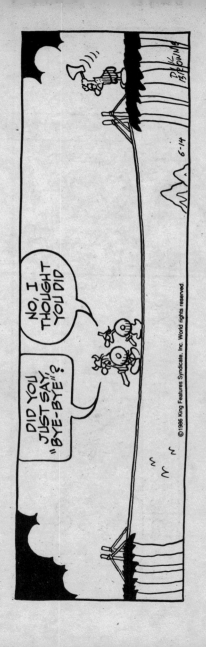

DIK BROWNE

JUST RUNNING DOWN TO THE LOCAL STORE FOR SOME MORE HORRIBLY GOOD CARTOON BOOKS, COLOUR ALBUMS, CALENDARS, DIARIES, REMINDER CALENDARS, GREETING CARDS, GIFTWRAP AND TAGS – ALL FEATURING ME OF COURSE!
WHY NOT JOIN ME BEFORE THE BARBARIANS GET THERE!